S0-BOC-560

Library of
Douglas & Jill Kaufman

Library
Douglas College Victoria

The Kuekumber Kids Meet

THE NUMBERASAURUS

© 1992 SCOTT E. SUTTON

Written and Illustrated
by
SCOTT E. SUTTON

Published by

SUTTON PUBLICATIONS, INC.

14252 CULVER DRIVE, SUITE A-644
IRVINE, CALIF., 92714

First Edition
ISBN 0-9617199-7-4

Copyright © 1992 by
Scott E. Sutton
All rights reserved

No part of this work may be reproduced or transmitted in any form or by any means, electronic or mechanical, including photocopying and recording, or by an information storage or retrieval system without permission in writing from the publisher.

For information about more books by
Scott E. Sutton contact
Sutton Studios at 800-566-9733

Printed in Hong Kong by South Sea International Press Ltd.

THE
NUMBERASAURUS

Meet the Kuekumbers

This is Kirky Kuekumber.
He'll be six soon.
When he sees an adventure
He's out the door ... zoom!

This is Katie Kuekumber
Who is now age four.
She asks lots of questions.
And then she asks more!

This here is Krumby,
The Kuekumber kids' dog.
He's a really great pooch
But he eats like a hog.

This is Kim,
The Kuekumber kids' mother.
She takes care of Katie
And Katie's big brother.

This is Karl,
The Kuekumber kids' pop.
He likes to build things
In his little workshop.

This is Kirky's
Best friend, Lance,
Who likes to wear
Big, baggy pants.

Katie, Kirky and Krumby Kuekumber
Had awakened early from their nighttime slumber.
They were down on the beach, by the ocean blue,
Playing in the sand. Lance was there, too.

They built sand castles until they were through.

"So," said Kirky, "now what should we do?"

"See that canyon," asked Lance, "with all the big trees?

Let's go explore it. Who's coming with me?"

2

"Let's go!" yelled Kirky. "It'll be fun."

So across the beach the kids did run,

Into the canyon full of big trees,

Where they heard chirping birds and buzzing bees.

3

But as they hiked further the forest did change.
It became like a jungle with plants that were strange.
They saw big animals they had not seen before.
"Look at that!" yelled Katie. "A dinosaur!"

4

"Ahh, you're here at last!" the dinosaur said.

"Hey, he talks!" said Katie, scratching her head.

"Oh, yes," he said. "I'm the Numberasaurus.

And you are in my secret dinosaur forest."

The Numberasaurus was bright green and blue.

He had a long neck and a long tail, too.

He had yellow spots and the kids could see

In each spot was a number from **1** to **20**.

"Okay," said Lance. "But what do you do?"

"I am here," he said, "to teach numbers to you.

Today I will teach you to count up to **20**.

There are more numbers than that but **20** is plenty."

"What's the difference between a number and letter?"
Asked Katie, who did not know any better.
"A letter is used to make words," said he.
"But a number shows you how many, you see?"

"Now to help me with my teaching chores
Will be **20** helper dinosaurs!
So let's get started, counting is fun.
Bring on Dinosaur Number **1**."

Out trotted Dinosaur Number **1**
Whose skin was yellow like the sun.
"I have **1** mouth so I can eat.
And **1** tail, too, behind on my seat."

Number **2** dinosaur flew on down.
She landed softly on the ground.
"I have **2** wings so that I can fly
Way up high in the bright blue sky."

Number **3** dinosaur came out and said,

"I have **3** horns up on my head."

"Yes, I see them!" said Kirky. "**1**, **2**, and **3**."

"Very good!" said Numberasaurus happily.

The Number **4** dinosaur was red and black
With **4** green stripes upon his back.
Dinosaur **5** yelled out as planned,
"I have **5** fingers on each hand."

Then came a big dinosaur, Number **6**,
Who had **6** toes and was munching on sticks.
Compared to **6**, dino **7** was small.
But he was still over **7** feet tall!

Dinosaur **8** and **9** then came.

They looked alike, almost the same.

"I have **8** spots upon my head.

And **9** has **9** spots," Number **8** said.

Dinosaur **10** weighed **10** tons or more!
When he walked he shook the forest floor.
Then came a tall dinosaur, Number **11**.
Who was **4** feet taller than Dinosaur **7**.

Dinosaurs Number **12** and **13**

Were the smallest dinosaurs the kids had seen.

Number **12** was only **12** inches tall,

While **13** was taller by **1** inch, that's all!

Dino **14** was huge, and walked out very slow.

With **14** plates on your back, how fast would you go?

Dino **15** looked mean. He was **15** feet tall.

He had big sharp teeth and eyes that were small.

Dinos **16** and **17** jumped without care,
Bouncing up high, **16** feet in the air.
Dino **17** shouted, "Today's my birthday.
I'm **17** years old now. Hip, hip, hooray!"

"Time's almost up!" Numberasaurus did shout.

"The rest of you dinosaurs, come on out."

They rushed out so fast, they all nearly fell,

Dinosuars **18**, **19**, and **20** as well.

"So there they all are," said the Numberasaurus. "Numbers **1** through **20**, right here before us. Now, let's count together: **1**, **2**, **3**, **4**, **5**, **6**, **7**, **8**. Keep counting, there's more."

"9, 10, 11, 12, and 13, 14, too.
15, 16, 17, 18, 19, 20. We're through!"
"Right," said Numberasaurus, "now one more time."
The kids counted out loud through 20 just fine.

"You've got it! You've got it! Now practice away.
And you'll be able to count past **100** some day!
But now it is time," said the Numberasaurus,
"For my friends and I to go back to our forest."

"Thank you," said Lance. "This counting is fun."
"You're welcome," said the dinosaurs one by one.
Then the forest and dinosaurs faded away.
"Talking dinosaurs," said Katie, "wow, what a day!"

The kids walked home, counting things on the beach
With the numbers the Numberasaurus did teach.
And that night at home with their family
The kids wondered where Numberasaurus could be.

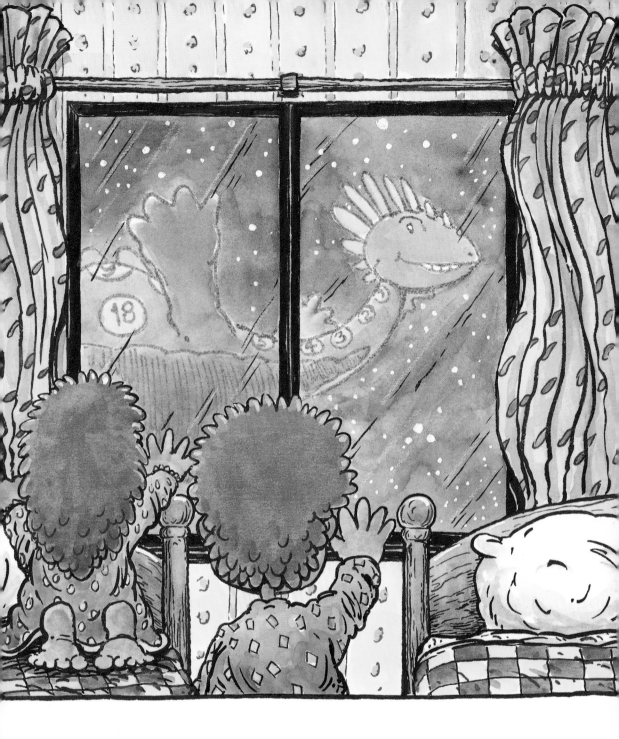

When Katie and Kirky climbed into their beds,
As they were about to lay down their heads,
They looked out the window towards the sky
And saw Numberasaurus waving goodbye.

Do you have these **Kuekumber Kids** books?

The Alphabet Alien

ISBN 0-9617199-0-7
Teaches about A,B,Cs

The Numberasaurus

ISBN 0-9617199-7-4
Teaches about numbers 1 - 20

The Professor of Paint

ISBN 0-9617199-8-2
Teaches about color

The Sheik of Shapes

ISBN 0-9617199-9-0
Teaches about shapes

To get these and other Scott E. Sutton books write for your free brochure to:

Sutton Publications, Inc. **14252 Culver Drive #A644** **Irvine, CA 92714**